Use tracing paper to foll

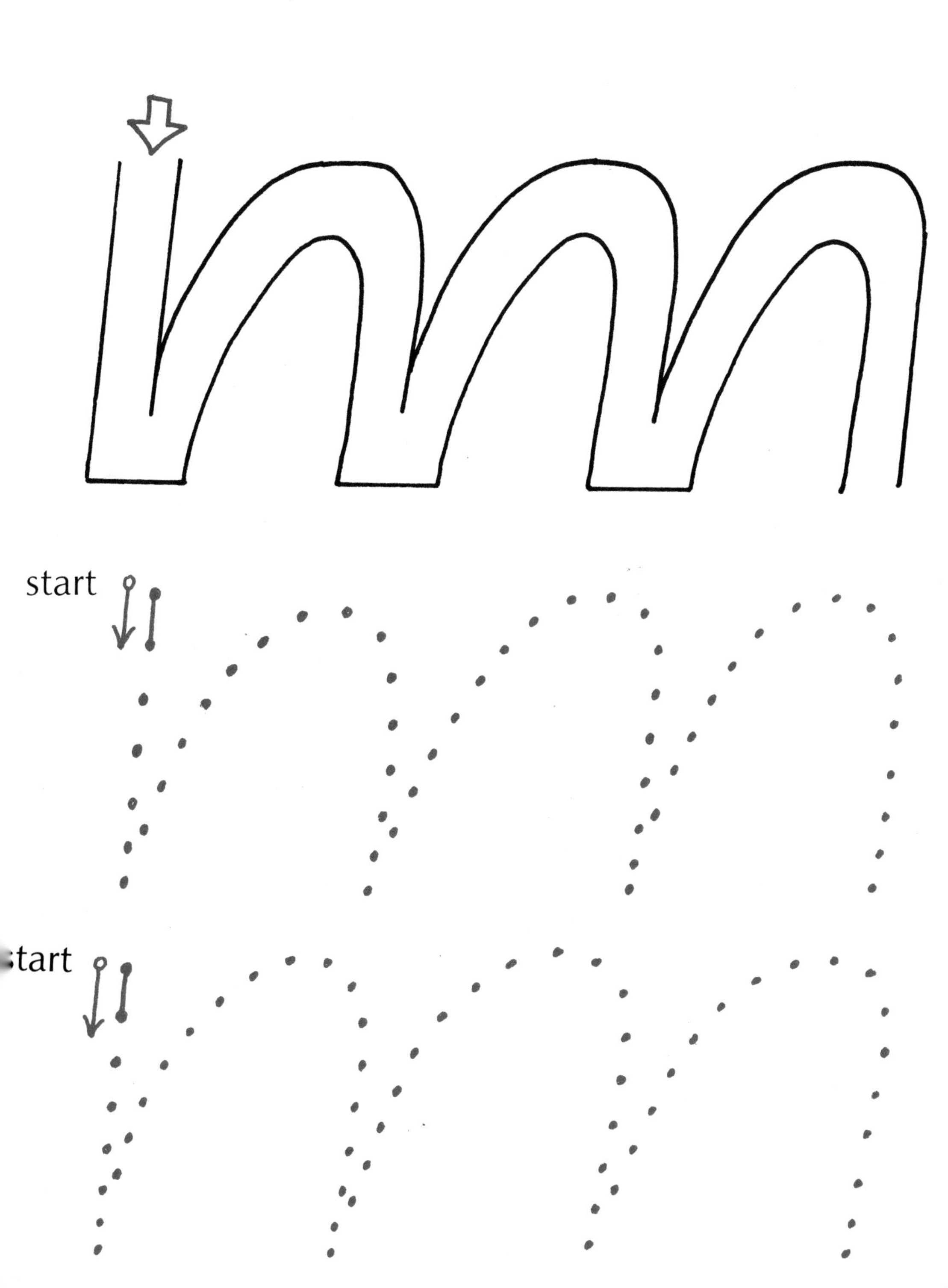

Copy the patterns.

r n m h b p

r n m h b p

This is the first family of letters.

mmm mmm mmm

mmm mmm mmm

r n r m h

b r p n

r n m h b p

r n m h b p

r n m h b p

r n m h b p

Use tracing paper to follow the maze.

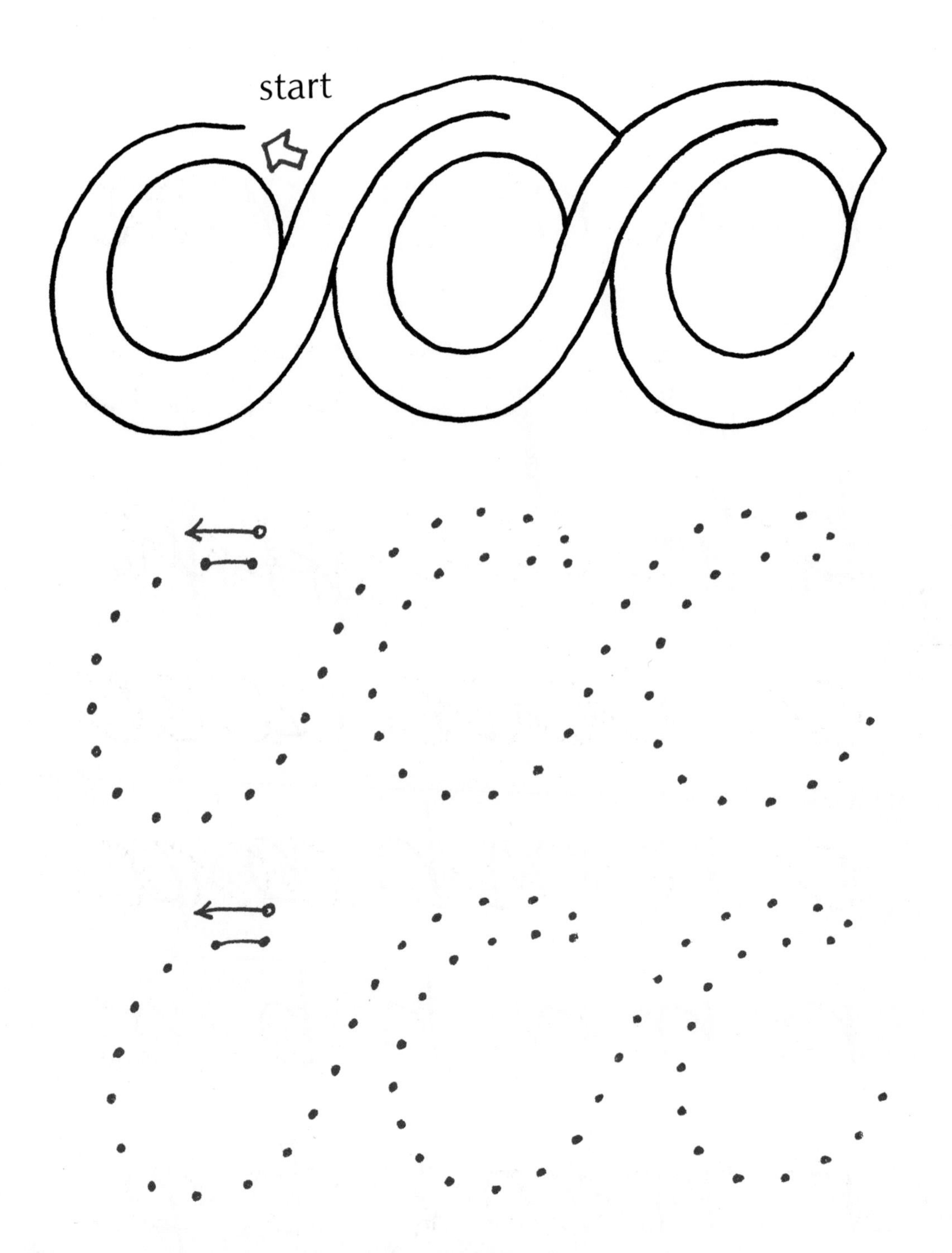

This is the second pattern.

This is the second family of letters.

ccc ccc ccc

ccc ccc ccc

c o C a g

d q c e

c o a g d q e

c o a g d q e

c o a g d q e

c o a g d q e

Some words to copy.

a man and a dog
grandma had a
bag

can a dog run
a bar on a cage
an open door
hand me a peg
or a good mop

Use tracing paper to follow the maze.

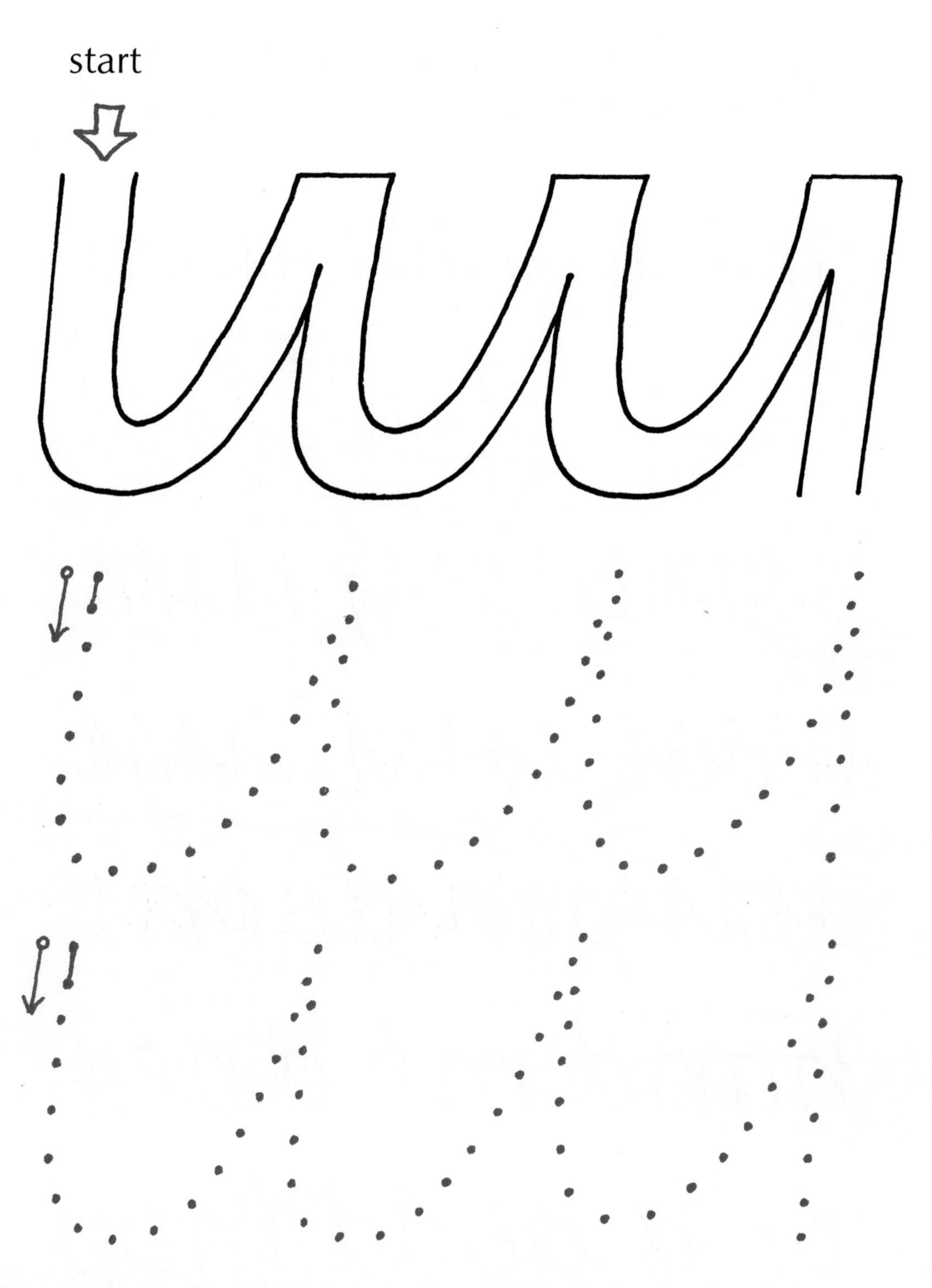

This is the third pattern.

i u y l t u

i u y l t u

This is the third family of letters.
Notice the t is a middle sized letter.

uuu uuu uuu

i u y l t u

i u u y l

t i u t

i u y l t u

i u y l t u

i u y l t u

lit till until it

Some more words to copy.

you may be ill

a little tree

open the lid

do tie it on

get me a lamp

until you go

lie in the hay

a cup and a bun

Use tracing paper to follow the maze.

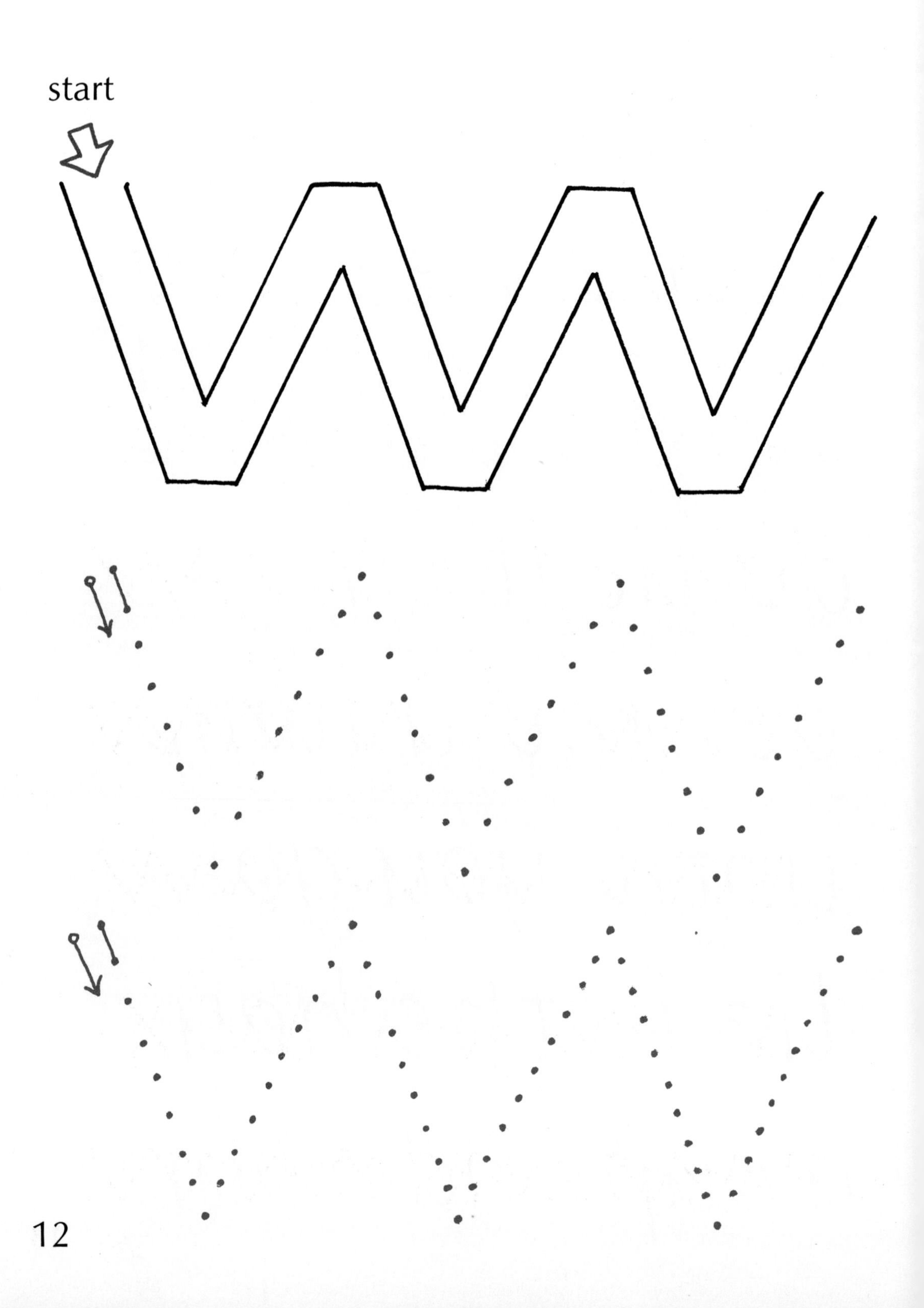

This is the fourth pattern.

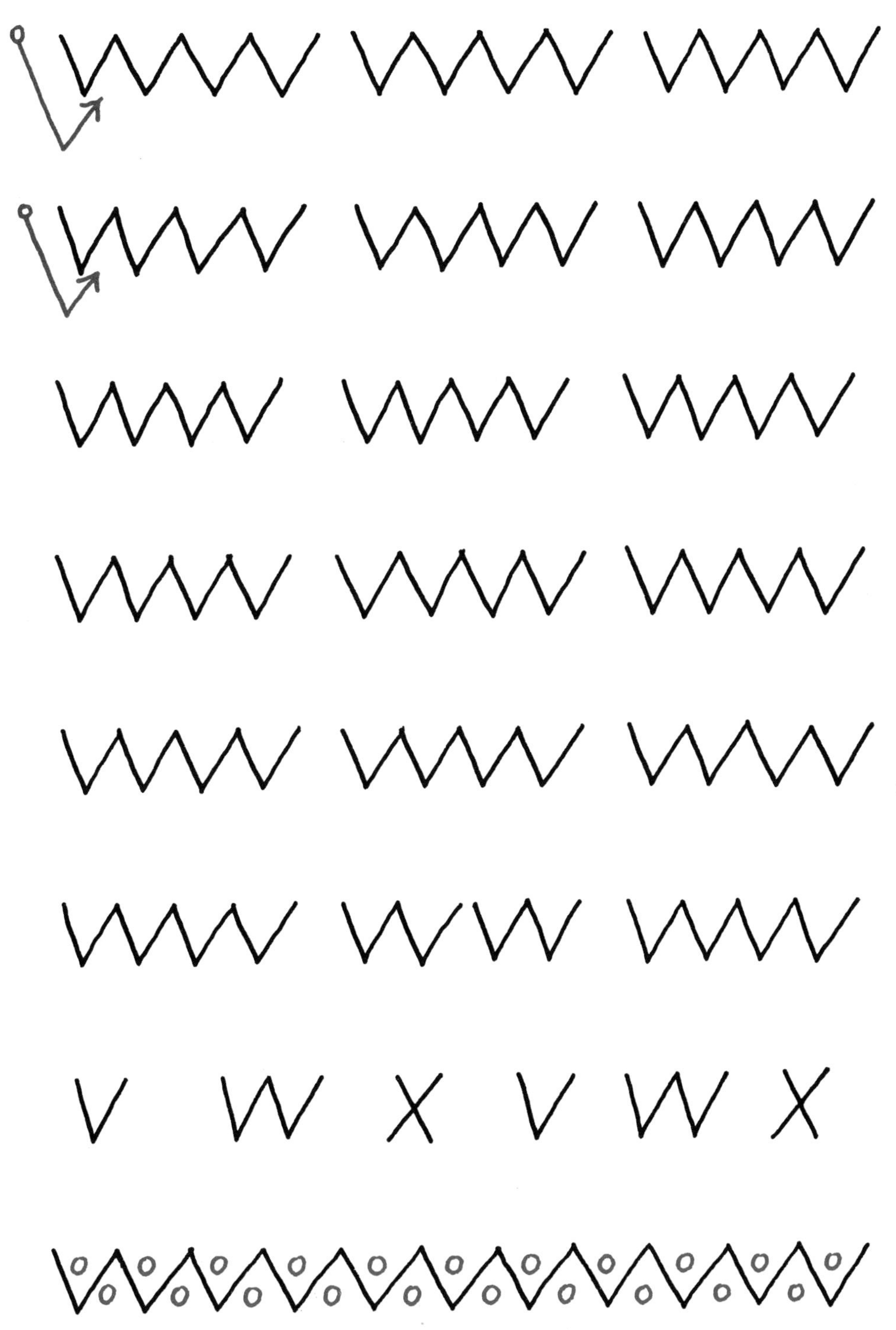

This is the fourth family of letters.

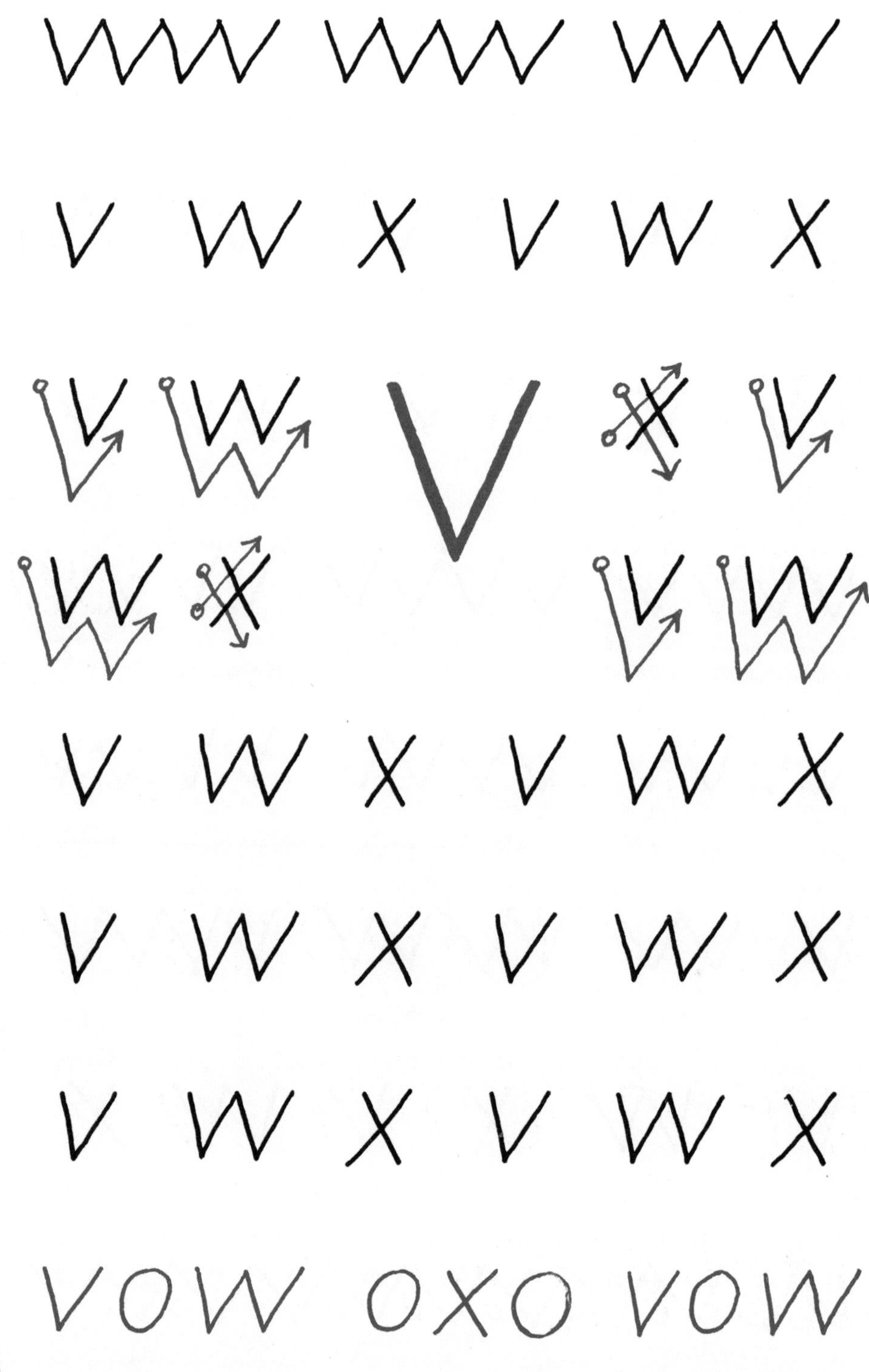

Some more words to copy.

you win a cow
a van and a man
can we mow
an axe will chop
wood 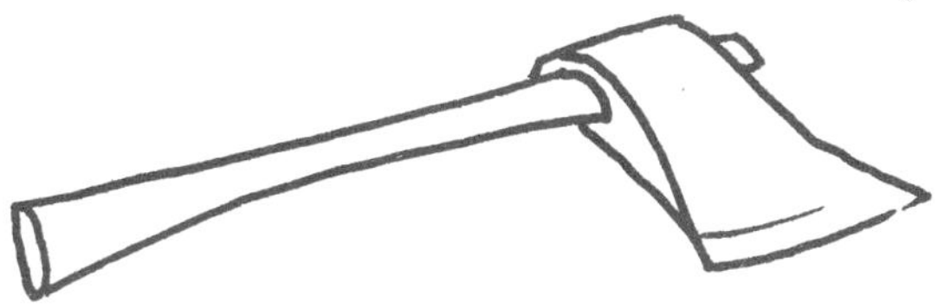
wax crayons
are good in a
little box

Use tracing paper to follow the maze.

This is the fifth pattern. Do not make the tall lines too high.

ullu ullu ullu

ullu ullu ullu

ullu ullu ullu

ullu ullu ullu

ullu ullu ullu

ullu ullu ullu

u y l t a d

a tall lady

This is the fifth family of letters.

u y l t

l a d y

u y l t a d

u y l t a d

u y l t a d

u y l t a d

Here are more words to copy.

run up the hill

will the cat lap

on a mat

will you get mad

can we go now

put mud in a bin

Use tracing paper to follow the maze.

This is the sixth pattern.

r n p r n p

rip pop nip up

This is the sixth family of letters.

r n p r n p

r n p r n p

r n p r n p

r n p r n p

This is the seventh pattern.

The eighth pattern.

The letter k. Notice this is the same height as h and b

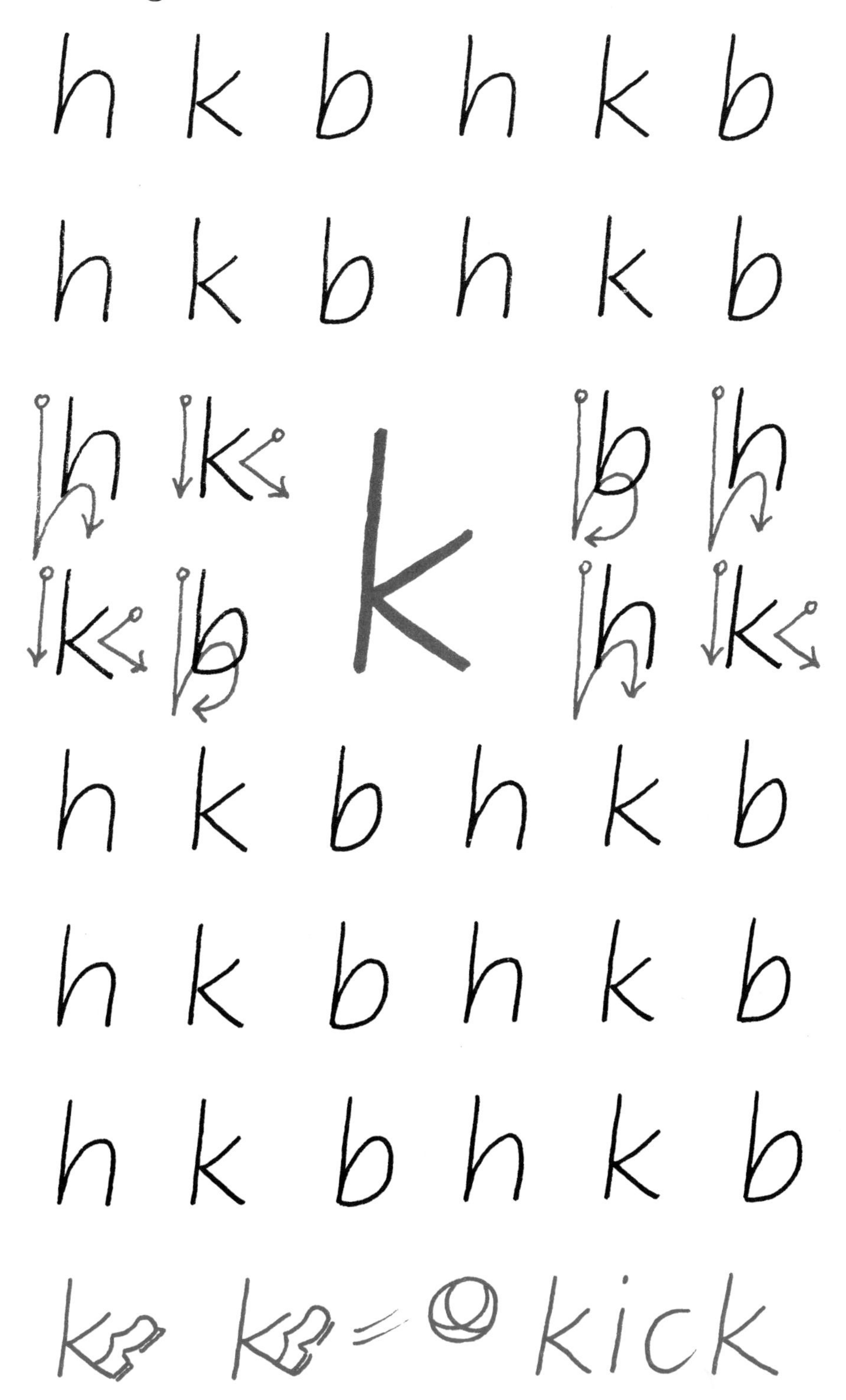

The letter f. The cross stroke is the same height as the letter m.

f m f m f m

f m f m f m

f m f f m

f m f m

f m f m f m

f m f m f m

f m f m f m

fee-fi-fo-fum

The letter t.
The cross stroke is the same height as the letter v.

t v t v t v

t v t v t v

t v t t v

t v t v

t v t v t v

t v t v t v

t v t v t v

television

Here is some more letter practice.
Do not make the tails of y and j
too long or too curly.

j i y j i y

j i y j i y

j j i y j

i y j j i

j i y j i y

j i y j i y

j i y j i y

jelly yumyum

Practise for the small letters s x and z

s x s z s w

s x s z s w

s x s s z

s w s x

s x s z s w

s x s z s w

s x s z s w

six whizzes

Some words to copy. All 26 letters of the alphabet are here. Can you make a sentence out of them?

lazy quick fox

over jumps

dog brown

the lazy over

quick the brown

fox jumps dog

Here is another sentence. Can you count all 26 letters of the alphabet in this one?

many big 
jackdaws 
quickly zipped
over the fox
pen.

A poem by Christina Rossetti.

Mix a pancake,
Stir a pancake,
Pop it in the pan.
Fry the pancake,
Toss the pancake,
Catch it if you can.

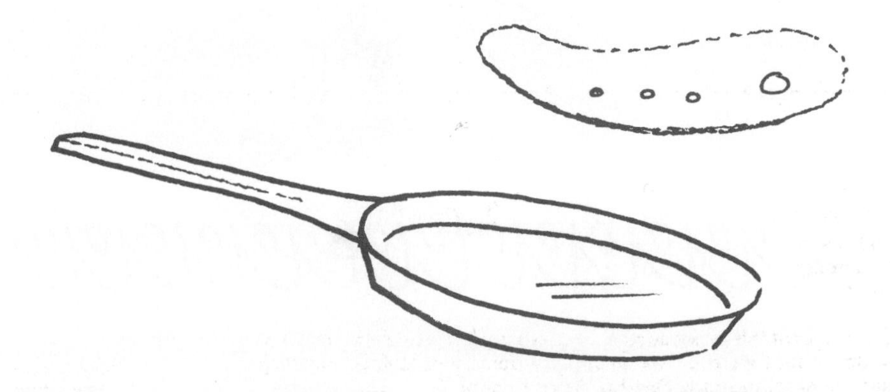

Printed in Hong Kong by Wing King Tong Co. Ltd